Y0-BZL-850

The Official Victory Glass

Price Guide

to

Antique Jukeboxes

An illustrated guide to the value of pre-1967 jukeboxes.

Pubisher
VICTORY GLASS INC.
3260 UTE AVENUE
WAUKEE, IA 50263 USA
PH: (515) 987-5765 FAX (515) 987-5762
Email: <vicglass@ix.netcom.com>
Website: <www.victoryglass.com>

ISBN 0-930181-05-0

Seventh Edition   **2000**

This seventh edition of the **Official Victory Glass Price Guide** is dedicated to my wife, Jan who has heard more jukebox tales than I am sure anyone would care to hear. Her never ending support and dedication to me has made my life's work not only a fun hobby and a great business, but a real passion that we share. I am so blessed to have her in my life.

Table of Contents

Introduction

You are holding in your hands the seventh edition of **The Official Victory Glass Price Guide to Antique Jukeboxes** for the year 2000! Now doesn't that make a jukebox that was manufactured in say 1939 sound old? It's been 25 years since I started in this hobby. In 1975 there were only a handful of jukebox collectors and if it didn't say the name "Wurlitzer" on it you probably didn't want to own it. Obviously many things have changed.

I often wonder what the "jukebox people" (the operators, the designers, the distributors) of those early days think about what has happened to the "business" of jukeboxes. Many of today's newcomers to the hobby fail to realize that when the jukeboxes were made they were intended only as a commercial piece of equipment. They were meant to be used for 10-12 years and then discarded. They were never intended to be kept, let alone restored and cared for by a collector as a valued antique. When Louis Tiffany made his famous leaded glass lamps in the early 1900's he wanted people to cherish them, to use them and to pass them on to future generations. He loved his work more than anyone and before his death he destroyed the very formulas he created to make these beautiful glass lamps saying that someday you will appreciate what you now have! Well the jukebox manufacturers also destroyed all their tooling, artwork and most of their records. The main difference however is that they never wanted people to keep those old jukeboxes. It was a strictly "business sense" philosophy. They needed to produce new models in order to stay in business. They never wanted to see those older jukeboxes alive. They were nothing more than an old washing machine that needed to be hauled away and buried. Boy, were they ever wrong!

Over the past 25 years since the hobby of collecting jukeboxes really began, there have been a lot of changes. Many hobbies will come and go (Beenie Babies, Furbies, etc.), some will linger on from the moment they are conceived (Baseball cards, Barbie dolls, etc.) and some sprout out of the junk pile. The hobby of collecting jukeboxes is like this later type. The old phrase "Another man's trash, is another man's treasure" sums up the jukebox hobby. For a quarter of a century now we have been actively buying, restoring and selling jukeboxes that most people never really wanted or believed they had much value.

Today we are of course still in love with those wonderful art deco designs of wood, plastic and metal from the 1930's and 1940's. The Wurlitzer Co. is still recognized as having made the best of The Golden Age Jukes. Paul Fuller (famous Wurlitzer designer) designed 13 models that played 24 selections from 1938 to 1948. He also was responsible for the 6 countertop models (inc. model 50) and a wide array of wallspeakers and wallboxes. The "light up" Wurlitzers are still the cream of the crop for the dedicated collector. Prices today after having fallen some 10 to 20% over the past 5 years are now once again on the increase. Many large collections have been sold by early collectors. The demand is not increasing like it used to, but the supply is very limited. As any well seasoned collector will tell you "the 40's boxes are really getting hard to find". We look for prices to continue rising as the classic 40's boxes, models such as the 1015, 1100, and 1080 are going to go back up in price.

In addition to the Wurlitzer models there are some fabulous machines made by other manufacturers you will want to look out for. The AMI Company produced some great models in the 30's/40's like the Top Flite, Streamliner and the famous Singing Towers. Rock-Ola made the majestic Premier, Commando and Spectrovox models along with some great wallspeakers. Seeburg had its rare Concert Master and 9800/9200 models. Also, don't overlook some of the really unique and truly collectible models made by Capehart, Gabels, Mills, Packard and other lesser known companies.

The old 78 rpm machines of the 1940's and before are at the heart of many collections, but equally as important are the "Silver Age" machines of the 1950's. Following the post war record productions of jukeboxes like the 1015 Wurlitzer, the AMI model "A", the Seeburg 146-7-8 models and the Rock-Ola 1422-26-28 models we saw the jukebox business take a step back. After all there were only so many locations to place a coin-operated jukebox. Out of the early 50's jukebox slump, we began to see some really great designs and some well built jukeboxes.

The jukeboxes of the 1950s are often characterized by extruding chrome and curved glass fronts. The AMI Company made some really bad designs from the early 50's (models D, E, F and G) but came back with the beautiful and highly prized H and I models. Rock-Ola made some mistakes as well in the early part of the decade but overall made some great boxes like the 1448, 1446, 1468 through 1485 (Tempo I and II) models. Wurlitzer couldn't decide on 78's or 45's for their models so came up with the really mediocre models 1250-1400-1600. They made an about turn and started making some of the best designs with models 1700, 1800, 1900, 2000, 2100 and 2104. Seeburg was the overall winner of jukebox manufacturer in the 1950"s. They consistently produced the most popular models of their day. They took a firm stand on the 45/78 rpm record dilemma and won. Today the model V200 (and VL200) are the most valuable of the silver age machines in the USA.

There are many wonderful models to collect from the 1940's and 1950's and although this is the focus of jukebox collecting today it is not all that there is. Don't forget the early wooden boxes of the 1930's. Seeburg made some fabulous art deco designs from that time. The early Rock-Ola and Wurlitzers with their "radio styled" cabinets are a great buy. I should mention here that the Wurlitzer "Debutante" model (first model made by Wurlitzer) is not cheap! One of only a few known to exist just sold in 1998 for over $40,000.00! That was the record price for a jukebox unless a 950 model brought that much!

In addition to the older boxes, there are a lot of people looking at the 60's models and newer. While early 60's AMI Continental and Rock-Ola Tempo models have been sought after for some time now, there is an increased level of interest in all 60's boxes. The prices are still low on most of these 60's models (under $500.00) and they are approaching 40 years old. Will these be the new hot collectibles?

FORECAST FOR THE FUTURE

Technology is changing the way we do business and that includes buying, selling and collecting old jukeboxes. We are finding the world to be a much smaller place than we thought. The buyers from Europe are here in the states buying boxes for their customer most every month. We have exported an estimated 50,000 machines, to Europe in the past 12 years. We have more customers and collectors in Holland than we do in New York. Antique jukeboxes are an international business and what happens around the world effects prices here in the USA. If it were not for the thriving business for nostalgia america in Holland, Germany, France, UK etc., we would see far lower prices in this guide. Like anything we grew up with we tend to take it for granted. Jukeboxes were an **American** invention and we all were used to seeing them. There were plenty and they were cheap. Sometimes it takes an outsider to see the value in something and to let us know how much it is really worth. I do not begrudge others for buying up our collectible jukeboxes. We do the same with other antiques from Europe that are brought here to the USA. I do wish there were more Americans that were willing to pay the price to keep more of these great jukeboxes here. We don't always know what we have until it's gone. Someday maybe we will be back in Europe buying back our old Wurlitzers.

The world of collecting has been brought to our computers. We now communicate by email. We can order parts and service manuals at interactive websites. We now buy and sell instantly with computer auction services such as Ebay. You no longer have to wait for the mailman to deliver your Always Jukin or Jukebox Collector magazine to see what's for sale. Technology is changing the way we do business in all facets of our lives - even collecting old jukeboxes.

From digital cameras to digital CD's the way we look at and collect jukeboxes is changing. The new models for the new millennium may not ever play CD's. The music will be downloaded to a micro chip or beamed from a satellite in orbit. Technology is great but don't let it erase the past. There is something to be said about the days when a jukebox lit up a room. It's magic glow embraced a would be dance floor and enticed patrons to deposit a coin or two. It was the drawing card that made people dance, fall in love, fight, drink, laugh, converse, gather, enjoy life, cry, celebrate, reminisce, ponder, shout, sweat, think and listen...In other words it brought out emotions. The jukebox was a major part of our culture and of our daily lives. It was more than just entertainment. It was more than a living for the operator. It added a great deal to our personal lives. It drew people closer as they gathered in a restaurant or bar or drug store. It was from a much simpler time in some ways. It reminds me of days when the radio and television stations were not full of obscenities, when Sunday was considered a holy day and most businesses were closed. It was a day when families got together to watch television and the kids hung out at the malt shop after school.

Most Americans strive to own the new house, the new car, the latest in technology—that is not all bad either. I enjoy the newest and latest as much as anyone—but I really love my old jukeboxes! Often times I shut down the THX movie theater, turn off the PC and the stereo. I dim the lights and turn on the old Wurlitzer and punch B5 and play "That'll Be The Day". Life is more fun with an old jukebox.

I hope you agree and if you don't own at least one old juke - you'll start collecting. Those of us that fell in love years ago can tell you how much fun it is. Prices are still a bargain on many models and are not expected to rise dramatically in the near future. The hobby is still very strong after 25 years. We distribute parts to over 17,000 customers and the list is growing every day. We hope this guide will help you in deciding what to buy, sell or trade. Use it as only a guide and not the gospel. Call, write, fax or email us with any questions here at **Victory Glass**, but better yet attend a Chicagoland jukebox show and see what all the excitement is about. Come see what makes us tick, see what makes a grown man cry. See what makes your wife cry when you bring home **another** jukebox! You will know you are a true collector when your house looks like mine and people start calling it a "museum". Be kind to that old jukebox (it's probably had a tough life) and **All The Best In Your Never Ending Pursuit of Antique Jukeboxes.**

Stephen K. Loots

Publisher

— 5 —

About the Prices

This book above all was written to decide that age old question — just what is it worth? How much should I pay or how much can I get for my jukebox? That has never been a question easily answered. Prices can vary from one month to another as well as with condition and location around the world.

Something is worth just what someone is willing to pay for it — not what someone is willing to take for it. Unfortunately, being the diverse group of people we are, it is not such a simple matter to assign one price to an item since we all may value it differently. We must then come up with an average or relative value for each grade or condition of each jukebox model.

This is to say that the prices listed for each grade of machine are based on **average selling** prices during the past year. Machines may bring significantly more or less at one time or another depending on whether the seller is knowledgeable of what he is selling. A purchase from a dealer or an auction may be significantly off from these prices due to human emotion or lack of knowledge. What these prices should tell you is that you should be able to buy (or sell) a machine in the stated condition for the stated price if you are a reasonably good buyer (seller).

No one will ever come up with a value guide that satisfies everyone. Most of the price guides I have seen on antiques and coin-operated machines are full of inconsistencies and inaccurate information when they come to jukeboxes. Simple facts such as dates of manufacture can be widely disputed. In this guide I have combined all my available resources and knowledge to give you the most accurate price guide available. I hope that in our next edition we can provide you with even more information. Use this guide as just that — don't hesitate to pay a little more or offer a little less for that particular jukebox you really want. I don't think I can ever come up with a formula that takes into account sentimental value.

About the Listings

In this guide we have listed all of the major manufacturers of jukeboxes made in the period from 1920 to 1966. We may have left out a few companies like Western Electric, Ristaucrat, Williams, etc. because we feel that these companies were not really "jukebox" manufacturers and the few machines that they did produce are not of interest to most jukebox collectors. We have also left out most of the hideaway models produced by the various manufacturers except where we felt there was an interest. Also you will notice there are no listings for remote equipment (wallboxes, speakers, etc.) Some of these items are extremely rare and it is difficult to establish "current" prices on all of these, but we do hope to include many of them in our next edition.

Information as well as surviving examples of many of the lesser known manufacturers of the thirties and forties is to say the least — difficult to obtain. Rather than ignore their contribution to the hobby, we have listed as many of these models as we know. Where you see the notation "insufficient Data," this means we were unable to calculate a value for them due to the lack of this model jukebox in existence or enough of them being sold or traded.

We have also included for each model listed the date of manufacture. Most models were introduced in the fall of the preceding year, but are recognized as being produced the following year (i.e., a Wurlitzer 750 may have been introduced in late 1940, but is considered a 1941 model). Some models were produced for more than one year, but this is usually the exception rather than the rule.

We have endeavored to correct any mistakes that were found in our previous editions of this guide such as production figures and dates of manufacture as well as include any models we may have missed. We have listed for many Wurlitzer models the known figures for the quantity of machines shipped from the factory. Most company records have since been destroyed and this pertinent information appears lost forever for other makes.

We have included illustrations (many with dimensions) of most of the "Big Four" manufacturers (AMI, Rock-Ola, Seeburg and Wurlitzer) in this guide. These can be found in the back of this book. Everyday there is a new book out on the hobby and the best of these are listed on the following pages. These books will be of great help in learning more about the various manufacturers and models. If you read the books, attend a show or two every year and read the **Jukebox Collector Magazine**, you'll be an expert in no time! Welcome to the weird and wonderful world of jukebox collecting!

AMI

MODEL F (1931-1933), 20 SEL Insufficient Data

MODEL FR (1934-1935), 20 SEL Insufficient Data

TOP FLIGHT (1936-1938)

GRADE 5	GRADE 4	GRADE 3	GRADE 2	GRADE 1
2000	4000	5000	6000	7000

STREAMLINER (1938-1939), 20 SEL (VERY RARE)

| 5000 | 7000 | 8500 | 9000 | 10000 |

SINGING TOWER (1940-1941) STD 20 SEL MODEL

| 3500 | 5000 | 6000 | 7500 | 8500 |

SINGING TOWER (1941-1942), 40 SEL (Rare-Double)

| 5000 | 9000 | 12000 | 15000 | 18000 |

MODEL A (1946-1948), 40 SEL

| 1200 | 2000 | 3000 | 4000 | 5000 |

MODEL B (1948-1949), 40 SEL

| 800 | 1500 | 2000 | 2750 | 3500 |

MODEL C (1950), 40 SEL

| 450 | 900 | 1500 | 2000 | 2500 |

MODEL D-40 (1951), 40 SEL

| 400 | 700 | 1200 | 1500 | 2000 |

MODEL D-80 (1951-1952), 80 SEL

| 450 | 750 | 1250 | 1600 | 2200 |

MODEL E-40 (1953), 40 SEL

| 400 | 700 | 1200 | 1500 | 2000 |

MODEL E-80 (1953), 80 SEL

| 450 | 750 | 1250 | 1600 | 2200 |

MODEL E-120 (1953), 120 SEL

| 450 | 800 | 1300 | 1700 | 2300 |

MODEL F-80 (1954), 80 SEL

| 450 | 750 | 1200 | 1600 | 2200 |

GRADE 5	GRADE 4	GRADE 3	GRADE 2	GRADE 1
MODEL F-120 (1954), 120 SEL				
450	800	1250	1700	2300
MODEL G-80 (1955), 80 SEL				
400	700	1100	1550	2000
MODEL G-120 (1955), 120 SEL				
450	750	1150	1600	2100
MODEL G-200 (1956), 200 SEL				
500	800	1200	1700	2200
MODEL H-100 (1957), 100 SEL				
1000	1800	2300	2900	3500
MODEL H-120 (1957), 120 SEL				
1050	1900	2400	3000	3600
MODEL H-200 (1957), 200 SEL				
1200	2000	2500	3200	3800
MODEL I-100 (1958), 100 SEL				
1100	1800	2500	3300	4000
MODEL I-120 (1958), 120 SEL				
1200	1900	2600	3400	4100
MODEL I-200 (1958), 200 SEL				
1400	2100	2700	3600	4300
MODEL I-200M (1958), 200 SEL				
1200	1900	2600	3400	4100
MODEL J-100 (1959), 100 SEL (STEREO)				
750	1250	1700	2400	3000
MODEL J-120 (1959) 120 SEL (STEREO)				
800	1300	1800	2500	3100
MODEL J-200 (1959) 200 SEL (STEREO)				
900	1400	1900	2600	3200
MODEL J-200M (1959), 200 SEL (MONO/STEREO)				
800	1300	1800	2500	3100

GRADE 5	GRADE 4	GRADE 3	GRADE 2	GRADE 1

MODEL K-100A (1960), 100 SEL (MONO/STEREO)

| 550 | 1200 | 1600 | 2300 | 2800 |

MODEL K-120 (1960), 120 SEL (MONO/STEREO)

| 600 | 1250 | 1700 | 2400 | 2900 |

MODEL K-200A (1960), 200 SEL (MONO/STEREO)

| 750 | 1300 | 1800 | 2500 | 3000 |

MODEL K-200E (1960), 200 SEL (MONO/STEREO)

| 750 | 1300 | 1800 | 2500 | 3000 |

MODEL K-200M (1960) 200 SEL (MONO/STEREO)

| 700 | 1250 | 1700 | 2400 | 2900 |

MODEL LYRIC (1961), 100 SEL (STEREO)

| 1000 | 1700 | 2300 | 2900 | 3500 |

MODEL CONTINENTAL (1961), 200 SEL (STEREO)

| 1100 | 2100 | 3100 | 3800 | 4800 |

MODEL LYRIC-2 (1962), 100 SEL

| 1000 | 1700 | 2300 | 2900 | 3500 |

MODEL CONTINENTAL-2 (1962), 100 SEL (33/45 RPM) (STEREO)

| 1000 | 2000 | 3000 | 3700 | 4700 |

MODEL CONTINENTAL-2 (1962), 200 SEL (33/45 RPM) 9STEREO)

| 1200 | 2200 | 3200 | 4000 | 5000 |

NOTE: Effective in 1962 the AMI Company became known as Rowe/AMI

MODEL JAL (1963), 200 SEL (STEREO)

| 500 | 850 | 1250 | 1750 | 2250 |

MODEL JEL (Late 1963), 200 SEL (STEREO)

| 500 | 850 | 1250 | 1750 | 2250 |

MODEL JBM-200 (1964), 200 SEL "Tropicana"

| 400 | 650 | 900 | 1200 | 1500 |

MODEL JAN-200 (1965), 200 SEL "Diplomat"

| 400 | 650 | 900 | 1200 | 1500 |

MODEL JAO-200 (1966), 200 SEL "Bandstand"

| 400 | 650 | 900 | 1200 | 1500 |

AIREON

MODEL 1200 "Airliner" (1946), 24 SEL

GRADE 5	GRADE 4	GRADE 3	GRADE 2	GRADE 1
800	1500	2300	3400	3800

MODEL 1200A "Super Deluxe Airliner" (1946-47), 24 SEL

900	1600	2500	3500	4000

MODEL 1207 "Fiesta" (1946-47), 24 SEL

600	1100	1700	2400	2800

MODEL 1207A "Fiesta Deluxe" (1947-48), 24 SEL

700	1200	1800	2500	3000

MODEL "Blonde Bombshell" (1947-48), 24 SEL
Insufficient Data

MODEL 1209A "Coronet 400" (1948), 24 SEL

500	750	1350	1750	2200

MODEL "Coronet 500" w/Tonar (1949), 24 SEL
Insufficient Data

CAPEHART

The Capehart Mfg. Co. of Fort Wayne, Indiana, produced their first juke-box in 1928 and produced many models into the late 30's. Very few of these seem to have survived - seldom does one see any of these sold in a restored condition. Due to this fact we cannot place any exact values on the machines made by Capehart, but we have listed those models we know of for your information. Note: most of the Capehart mechanisms were non-selective (continuous play). CM=Counter Model.

Model 28F (1928) 56 SEL
Model 28G (1929) 56 SEL
Model 28GB (1929) 56 SEL
Model #1 (Prior to 1935) 10 SEL
Model #4 CM (Prior to 1935) 10 SEL
Model #5 Amperion (Prior to 1935) 24 SEL
Model #11 (Prior to 1935) 12 SEL
Model #11 Amperion (Prior to 1935) 24 SEL
Model #100 100 1/2 Amperion (Prior to 1935) 24 SEL
Model #101, 101 1/2 Amperion (Prior to 1935) 24 SEL
Model #110, 110 1/2 Amperion (Prior to 1935) 24 SEL
Model #111, 111 1/2 Amperion (Prior to 1935) 24 SEL

GRADE 5	GRADE 4	GRADE 3	GRADE 2	GRADE 1

Model #120, 120 1/2 Amperion (Prior to 1935) 24 SEL
Model #130, 130 1/2 Amperion (Prior to 1935) 24 SEL
Model #140, 140 1/2 Amperion (Prior to 1935) 24 SEL
Model #180, 180 1/2 CM (Prior to 1935) 10 SEL
Model #182, 182 1/2 CM (Prior to 1935) 10 SEL
Orchestrope, AIW (1936) 10 SEL
Orchestrope, B.I.W. (1936) 10 SEL
Orchestrope, M.I.W. (1936) 10 SEL
Orchestrope, C10-20 (1937) 24 SEL
Orchestrope, CA 10-20 (1937) 24 SEL

H.C. EVANS CO.

MODEL Constellation 951 (1949-50), 40 SEL (78 RPM)

700	1000	1700	2500	3000

MODEL Constellation 951 (1951), 40 SEL (45 RPM)

700	1000	1700	2500	3000

MODEL Jubilee 245 (1952-54),40 SEL (45 RPM)

700	950	1400	1900	2400

MODEL Jubilee 278 (1952-54), 40 SEL (78 RPM)

700	950	1400	1900	2400

MODEL Century 2045 (1952-54), 100 SEL (45 RPM)

750	1000	1500	2000	2500

MODEL Holiday (1954-55), 100 SEL (45 RPM)
Insufficient Data

MODEL Jewel 445 (1954-55), 50 SEL (45 RPM)
Insufficient Data

FILBEN

MAESTRO (1946-48), 30 SEL

3500	5000	6000	7000	8000

MODEL "Miracle Music" Remote Unit (1947-48), 30 SEL

4000	5000	6000	7000	8000

GRADE 5	GRADE 4	GRADE 3	GRADE 2	GRADE 1

JOHN GABEL CO.

EARLY ENTERTAINERS (1906-1916), 24 SEL
w/Needle changers complete with standard oak cabinet

5000	8000	10000	12500	15000

Note: Prices on the following models cannot be accurately determined due to their rarity.

GABLE, JR. (1929-30), 12 SEL
COMMERCIAL (1929-30), 24 SEL
ENTERTAINER (1929-30), SEL
GABLE JR., STANDARD (1931-33), 12 SEL
GABLE JR., MODERN (1933-34), 24 SEL
GABLE JR., SHERATON (1933-34), 24 SEL
STARLITE (1933), 12 SEL
ENTERTAINER (1935), 24 SEL
STREAMLINE (1936), 12 SEL
ELITE (1936), 18 SEL
ARISTOCRATE (1936), 24 SEL
LORELEI (1936), 12 SEL
CHARME (1937), 18 SEL
RAINBOW (1938-39), 24 SEL
KURO (1940), 24 SEL (very rare)

HOLCOMB AND HOKE

ELECTROMUSE (1926-27), 10 SEL

1000	1650	2250	2750	3500

MILLS

HI BOY (Non-Selective Models 800-801)
   (Models 870-871) (Models 864-865) (1928-29), 12 SEL
                    Insufficient Data
TROUBADOUR MODELS (1930-1934), 12 SEL
                    Insufficient Data

DANCE MASTER (1935), 12 SEL
DANCE MASTER (1936) 12 SEL
DANCE MASTER (DELUXE) (1936), 12 SEL
SWING KING (1936), 12 SEL
DO RE MI (1937), 12 SEL
                (The above five models generally sell for)

350	600	900	1200	1500

GRADE 5	GRADE 4	GRADE 3	GRADE 2	GRADE 1
STUDIO (1937), 12 SEL				
1300	2000	2800	3300	4000
ZEPHYR (1938), 12 SEL				
350	600	900	1200	1500
THRONE OF MUSIC (1939-40), 20 SEL				
900	1500	2250	3000	3500
EMPRESS (1940-41), 20 SEL				
1250	2000	2750	3750	4250
PANORAM (1940-42) (16 mm films with sound)				
3000	6000	9000	12000	15000
CONSTELLATION (950,951) (1946-47), 40 SEL				
700	1000	1700	2500	3000

PACKARD

GRADE 5	GRADE 4	GRADE 3	GRADE 2	GRADE 1
MODEL 7 PLA-MOR (1946-47), 24 SEL				
2500	3600	4500	5000	6000
MODEL 400 (HIDEAWAY) (1947-48), 24 SEL				
600	700	800	900	1000
MANHATTAN (1947-48), 24 SEL				
2500	3300	4500	5500	6500

ROCK-OLA

GRADE 5	GRADE 4	GRADE 3	GRADE 2	GRADE 1
MULTI SELECTOR (MODEL A) (1935), 12 SEL				
600	950	1500	2000	2500
REGULAR (1936), 12 SEL				
550	850	1300	1800	2200
NIGHT CLUB (1936), 12 SEL				
550	850	1300	1800	2200
RHYTHM KING 12 (1937), 12 SEL				
550	850	1300	1800	2250
RHYTHM KING 16 (1937), 12 SEL				
600	900	1350	1850	2300

GRADE 5	GRADE 4	GRADE 3	GRADE 2	GRADE 1

RHYTHM MASTER 12 (137), 12 SEL

| 550 | 850 | 1300 | 1800 | 2250 |

RHYTHM MASTER 16 (1937), 16 SEL

| 600 | 900 | 1350 | 1850 | 2300 |

AMBASSADOR (1937), 16 SEL

| 600 | 1000 | 1400 | 2000 | 2400 |

IMPERIAL 16 (1937), 16 SEL

| 550 | 850 | 1300 | 1800 | 2250 |

IMPERIAL 20 (1938), 20 SEL

| 600 | 900 | 1400 | 1900 | 2400 |

WINDSOR (1938), 20 SEL

| 700 | 1000 | 1500 | 2000 | 2500 |

MONARCH (1938), 20 SEL

| 700 | 1000 | 1500 | 2000 | 2500 |

'38 COUNTER MODEL (RED PALSTICS) (1938), 12 SEL

| 1250 | 1750 | 2200 | 3000 | 4000 |

'39 COUNTER MODEL (1939), 12 SEL

| 1500 | 2000 | 2750 | 3750 | 4500 |

LUXURY LIGHT-UP, STANDARD (1939), 20 SEL

| 850 | 1500 | 2400 | 3000 | 3800 |

LUXURY LIGHT-UP, DELUXE (1939), 20 SEL

| 900 | 1600 | 2500 | 3200 | 4000 |

JUNIOR 40 COUNTER MODEL (1940), 12 SEL

| 1500 | 2000 | 2750 | 3750 | 4500 |

'40 SUPER (W) (1940-41), 20 SEL

| 1200 | 2000 | 2750 | 3750 | 4500 |

'40 MASTER (W) (1940-41), 20 SEL

| 1200 | 2000 | 2750 | 3750 | 4500 |

'40 MASTER ROCKOLITE (1940), 20 SEL

| 1000 | 1800 | 2600 | 3600 | 4250 |

GRADE 5	GRADE 4	GRADE 3	GRADE 2	GRADE 1

PREMIER (1942), 20 SEL (VERY RARE)

| 14000 | 17500 | 22500 | 26000 | 30000 |

JR-12 COUNTER MODEL (1941), 12 SEL

| 1500 | 2250 | 3000 | 4000 | 4750 |

COMMANDO (1942), 20 SEL

| 5000 | 7500 | 10000 | 12500 | 15000 |

PRESIDENT (1942), 20 SEL
Only two machines known to exist - VALUABLE!

PLAYMASTER (HIDEAWAY) (1941-42), 20 SEL
(used in conjunction with Spectrovox - see below)

SPECTROVOX W/PLAYMASTER (1941-42), 20 SEL

| 8500 | 12000 | 16000 | 20000 | 25000 |

1422 (1946), 20 SEL

| 1500 | 2500 | 3500 | 4500 | 5500 |

1424 (HIDEAWAY) (1946-47), 20 SEL

| 400 | 600 | 700 | 750 | 800 |

1426 (1947), 20 SEL

| 1600 | 2700 | 3700 | 4750 | 5750 |

1428 (1948), 20 SEL

| 1700 | 2850 | 3900 | 4900 | 6000 |

1432 ROCKET (1950), 50 SEL

| 700 | 1100 | 2000 | 2800 | 3500 |

1434 SUPER ROCKET (1950-52), 50 SEL

| 750 | 1200 | 2200 | 3000 | 3700 |

1436 FIREBALL (1952), 120 SEL

| 750 | 1300 | 2300 | 3000 | 3800 |

1436A FIREBALL (1953), 120 SEL

| 800 | 1300 | 2300 | 3000 | 3800 |

1438 COMET (1954), 120 SEL

| 900 | 1500 | 2500 | 3400 | 4000 |

GRADE 5	GRADE 4	GRADE 3	GRADE 2	GRADE 1
1442 (1954), 50 SEL				
700	1200	2000	2600	3200
1446 (1954), 120 SEL				
900	1500	2500	3400	4000
1448 (1955), 120 SEL				
900	1500	2400	3000	3800
1452 (1956), 120 SEL				
850	1300	2200	2800	3500
1454 (1956), 120 SEL				
850	1300	2200	2800	3500
1455 (1957), 200 SEL				
900	1450	2400	3000	3700
1457 (1957), 100 SEL				
700	1200	1700	2400	3000
1458 (1958), 120 SEL				
650	1000	1700	2400	3000
1462 (1958), 50 SEL				
600	900	1500	2200	2800
1464 WALL JUKEBOX (1958)				
900	1500	2000	2500	3000
1465 (1958), 200 SEL				
700	1200	1700	2400	3000
1468 (1959), 120 SEL, TEMPO I (HI-FI/STEREO)				
1000	1800	2400	3000	3800
1475 (1959), 200 SEL, TEMPO I (HI-FI/STEREO)				
1200	2000	2600	3200	4000
1478 (1960), 120 SEL, TEMPO II (STEREO)				
1200	2000	2600	3300	4000
1485 (1960), 200 SEL, TEMPO II (STEREO)				
1250	2100	2700	3400	4200

GRADE 5	GRADE 4	GRADE 3	GRADE 2	GRADE 1

1484/403 (1960), 100 SEL, WALL JUKEBOXES (STEREO)

900	1500	2000	2500	3000

1488 (1961), 120 SEL, REGIS (STEREO)

800	1400	2000	2600	3200

1495 (1961), 200 SEL, REGIS (STEREO)

900	1500	2200	2800	3500

1496 (1962), 120 SEL, EMPRESS (STEREO)

750	1250	1800	2400	3000

1497 (1962), 200 SEL, EMPRESS (STEREO)

800	1350	2000	2600	3200

1493 (1962), 100 SEL, PRINCESS (STEREO)

750	1100	1600	2300	2900

404 (1963), 100 SEL, CAPRI (33/45 RPM)

400	750	1100	1400	1900

408 (1963), 160 SEL, RHAPSODY (33/45 RPM)

500	800	1200	1500	2000

414/414S (1964), 100 SEL, CAPRI II

400	750	1100	1400	1900

418/418SA (1964), 160 SEL, RHAPSODY II

500	800	1200	1500	2000

424 (1964), 100 SEL, PRINCESS ROYAL

500	800	1000	1200	1600

425 (1964), 160 SEL, GRAND PRIX

400	600	800	1000	1250

426 (1965), 160 SEL, GRAND PRIX II

400	600	800	1000	1250

429 (1965), 100 SEL, STARLET

450	750	1000	1250	1500

431 (1966-67), 100 SEL, CORONADO

350	550	750	950	1200

GRADE 5	GRADE 4	GRADE 3	GRADE 2	GRADE 1

432 (1966-67), 160 SEL, GP/160

400	600	800	1000	1250

433 (1966), 160 SEL, GP/IMPERIAL

400	600	800	1000	1250

NOSTALGIA 1000 (1987-89, 100 SEL) (1050 LOOK-A-LIKE)

1000	2000	2800	3200	3600

SEEBURG

AUDIOPHONE SERIES (1928-32), 8 SEL

1000	1750	2500	3000	3500

MELOPHONE SERIES (1930-31), 12 SEL

750	1400	1750	2250	2750

SELECTOPHONE SERIES (1932-35), 10 SEL

900	1300	1700	2200	2600

SYMPHONOLA SERIES (1935-37), 10 SEL
(Various Art Deco Models)

1000	2000	3000	4000	5000

K-20 (1936-37), 20 SEL

1000	1600	2400	3200	3800

REX (1937), 20 SEL

800	1300	1800	2500	3000

ROYALE (1937), 20 SEL

800	1300	1800	2400	3000

CONCERT GRAND (1938), 20 SEL

950	1500	2250	3000	4000

REGAL (1938), 20 SEL

800	1300	2000	2800	3400

GEM (1938), 20 SEL

700	1100	1500	2200	2600

CROWN (1938), 20 SEL

900	1400	2000	2800	3600

GRADE 5	GRADE 4	GRADE 3	GRADE 2	GRADE 1
PLAZA (1939), 20 SEL				
800	1300	1800	2400	3000
CLASSIC (1939), 20 SEL				
900	1400	2000	2800	3600
MAYFAIR (1939), 20 SEL				
800	1300	1800	2400	3000
VOGUE (1939), 20 SEL				
900	1400	2000	2800	3600
CASINO (1939), 20 SEL				
800	1200	1600	2200	2800
CADET (1940), 20 SEL				
900	1500	2400	3200	4000
MAJOR (1940), 20 SEL				
900	1500	2400	3200	4000
ENVOY (1940), 20 SEL				
900	1500	2400	3200	4000
COMMANDER (1940), 20 SEL				
1000	1750	2650	3650	4300
COLONEL (1940), 20 SEL				
950	1600	2500	3400	4200
CONCERT MASTER (1940), 20 SEL				
5000	6500	8000	10000	12000
MODEL 7800 (1941), 20 SEL				
800	1600	2400	3200	4000
MODEL 7850 (1941), 20 SEL				
800	1600	2400	3200	4000
MODEL 8800 (1941), 20 SEL				
800	1600	2400	3200	4000
MODEL 9800 (1941), 20 SEL				
900	1600	2400	3200	4000

GRADE 5	GRADE 4	GRADE 3	GRADE 2	GRADE 1
MODEL 8200 (1942), 20 SEL				
1500	2000	3000	4000	5000
MODEL 9200 (1942), 20 SEL				
1500	2000	3000	4000	5000
'43 CABINET (1943), 20 SEL				
750	1250	1500	1800	2250
146 SERIES (WOOD CABINETS) (1946), 20 SEL				
600	1000	1800	2500	3500
147 SERIES (WOOD OR METAL CABINETS) (1947), 20 SEL				
600	1000	1800	2500	3500
148 SERIES (METAL CABINETS - BLONDE) (1948), 20 SEL				
600	1050	1900	2600	3600

Note: There were many variations made with the 146, 147 and 148 models but prices seem to be constant between the different models.

GRADE 5	GRADE 4	GRADE 3	GRADE 2	GRADE 1
M100A (1949-50), 100 SEL				
500	900	1750	2750	3500
MODELS M100B, BL (1950-51), 100 SEL				
700	1000	2200	3200	4000
MODEL M100C (1952), 100 SEL				
950	1500	3000	4000	5250
MODEL W-100 (1953), 100 SEL				
850	1500	2400	3600	4500
MODEL HF-100G (1953), 100 SEL				
850	1400	2300	3500	4400
MODEL HF-100R (1954), 100 SEL				
950	1500	2800	3600	4500
MODEL J-100 (DARK FINISH) (1955) 100 SEL				
900	1300	2200	3200	4000
MODEL JL-100 (LIGHT FINISH) (LATE 1955), 100 SEL				
900	1400	2300	3300	4100

GRADE 5	GRADE 4	GRADE 3	GRADE 2	GRADE 1
MODEL V-200 (1955), 200 SEL				
2500	4500	5500	7000	8500
MODEL VL-200 (1956), 200 SEL				
2400	4300	5300	6600	8000
MODEL KD-200, KS-200 (1957). 200 SEL				
1400	2250	3250	4250	5000
MODEL L-100 (1957), 100 SEL				
700	1000	1750	2500	3200
MODEL 101 (1957-58), 100 SEL				
700	1000	1750	2500	3200
MODEL 161 (1958), 160 SEL				
900	1750	2600	3400	4200
MODEL 201 (1958), 200 SEL				
1000	2000	3000	3600	4400
MODEL 220 (1959), 100 SEL (STEREO)				
900	1500	2350	3300	3900
MODEL 222 (1959), 160 SEL (STEREO)				
950	1700	2500	3500	4200
MODEL AQ100 (1959), 100 SEL (STEREO)				
300	700	1350	1800	2300
MODEL AQ160 (1960), 160 SEL, (STEREO)				
450	800	1500	2000	2500
MODEL AY100 (1961), 100 SEL (STEREO)				
350	750	1450	1900	2400
MODEL AY160 (1961), 100 SEL (STEREO)				
450	850	1600	2100	2600
MODEL DS100 (1962), 100 SEL (STEREO)				
350	750	1450	1900	2400
MODEL DS160 (1962),160 SEL (STEREO)				
450	850	1600	2100	2600

MODEL LPC1/LPC1R (1963), 160 SEL (STEREO)

300	600	900	1200	1500

MODEL U-100 (1964),100 SEL "Mustang"

400	750	1000	1250	1500

MODEL LPC-480 (1964), 160 SEL

300	600	900	1200	1500

MODEL PFEA1U (Electra) and APFEA1 (Fleetwood) (1965-66), 160 SEL "Discoteque"

300	600	900	1200	1500

MODEL SS-160 (1966), 160 SEL, "Stereo Showcase"

300	600	900	1200	1500

MODEL SCCD-1 Classic (1988-90) (1015 LOOK-A-LIKE) (CDs)

1500	2000	2500	3000	4000

UNITED MFG. CO.

MODEL UPA 100 (1957-58), 100 SEL

500	900	1200	1700	2400

MODEL UPB 100 (1959), 100 SEL

500	900	1200	1700	2400

MODEL UPC 100 (1960), 100 SEL

600	1000	1300	1800	2500

MODEL UPD-100 (1961-63), 100 SEL

Insufficient Data

WURLITZER

Note: When available, production figures will follow the year of manufacture.

DEBUTANTE (1933), 10 SEL
Note: Very rare - only a few known to exist.
A mint original recently sold at auction for a record price of $42,900
(inc. 10% buyers fee)

10/P-10 (1934-35), 10 SEL

1500	2250	3000	4000	5000

Note: A mint original recently sold at auction for a record price of $8,860
(inc. 10% buyers fee)

GRADE 5	GRADE 4	GRADE 3	GRADE 2	GRADE 1
P-20 (1934-35), 10 SEL				
2000	3000	3750	4500	5000
P-30 (1935), 12 SEL				
2250	3500	4000	4750	5500
P-12 (1935), 12 SEL				
750	1200	1800	2500	2900
P-400 (1935) 12 SEL				
1500	2000	2500	3000	3900
35 (1936), [99], 12 SEL				
2000	2500	3500	4500	5000
400 (1936), 12 SEL				
1500	2000	2500	3000	3900
312 (1936), [7755], 12 SEL				
700	1000	1500	2200	2750
412 (1936), 12 SEL				
800	1200	1750	2400	3000
316 (1937), 16 SEL				
800	1200	1700	2300	2900
416 (1937), [1003], 16 SEL				
900	1300	1900	2600	3200
616 (1937), [23,706], 16 SEL				
600	900	1400	2000	2500
616-A (1937), 16 SEL				
600	900	1400	2000	2500
716 (1937), [2600], 16 SEL				
1000	1500	2250	3000	3750
50 (1938), 12 SEL				
2000	3000	4000	5000	6000
51 COUNTER MODEL (1938), 12 SEL				
1600	2000	2500	3500	4500

GRADE 5	GRADE 4	GRADE 3	GRADE 2	GRADE 1
61 COUNTER MODEL (1938-39), [8260], 12 SEL				
1300	2000	3000	4000	5000
24 (1938), 24 SEL				
1500	2250	3500	4500	5250
24-A (1938), 24 SEL				
1500	2250	3500	4500	5250
P-500, P-500A (1938-39), 24 SEL				
1300	2000	3000	4500	5500
G-500, G-500A (1938-39), 24 SEL				
1400	2200	3200	4800	5800
600, 600-A (1938-39), [9777-600 only], 24 SEL				
1000	1800	2600	4000	5000
K-600, K-600-A (1939), 24 SEL				
1000	1800	2600	4000	5000
41 COUNTER MODEL (1940-41), [2010], 12 SEL				
3000	3800	4500	6000	7000
41-H (HOME COUNTER MODEL) (1940), 12 SEL				
3000	3800	4500	6000	7000
71 COUNTER MODEL (1940-41), [4506], 12 SEL				
4000	5000	6000	7250	8500
700 (1940), [9498], 24 SEL				
2000	3000	4000	5200	6200
800 (1940), [11,501], 24 SEL				
3500	4500	6000	7500	8500
750 (1941), [6411], 24 SEL				
3500	4500	6000	7500	8500
750-E (1941), [11,976], 24 SEL				
3500	4500	6000	7500	8500
780 (1940-41), 24 SEL				
2500	3500	4500	5500	6500

GRADE 5	GRADE 4	GRADE 3	GRADE 2	GRADE 1
780-E (1940-1942), 24 SEL				
2500	3500	4500	5500	6500
850 (1941), [10,002], 24 SEL				
9000	12500	15000	17500	20000
850-A (1941), [456], 24 SEL				
10000	14000	18000	19000	22000
81 COUNTER MODEL (1941), [918], 12 SEL				
6000	7000	8000	9000	10000
950 (1942), [3497], 24 SEL				
20000	2500	24000	26000	30000
VICTORY (1942-45), 16 SEL/ROTARY				
3500	5000	6500	7750	8500
VICTORY (1942-45), 24 SEL/ROTARY				
3750	5500	7000	8250	9000
VICTORY (1942-45), 24 SEL/KEYBOARD				
3750	5500	7000	8250	9000
1015 (1946-47), [56,246], 24 SEL				
4000	5500	7500	9500	10500
1017 HIDEAWAY (1946-47), 24 SEL				
800	1000	1500	N/A	N/A
1080 (1947), [7604, including A&C Models], 24 SEL				
4800	5800	7000	8500	9500
1080-A (1947-48), 24 SEL				
4800	5800	7000	8500	9500
1080-C (1948), 24 SEL				
5800	7000	8000	9000	10000
1017-A HIDEAWAY (1947-48), 24 SEL				
800	1000	1500	N/A	N/A
1100 (1947-49), [27,000 estimated], 24 SEL				
3000	4000	5000	6500	7500

GRADE 5	GRADE 4	GRADE 3	GRADE 2	GRADE 1
1250 (1950), [13,496], 48 SEL				
700	1000	2000	3000	3500
1400 (1951-52), [10,219], 48 SEL				
850	1200	2300	3300	3800
1450 (1951-52), [4085], 48 SEL				
750	1100	2250	3200	3700
1500 (1952-53), 104 SEL				
800	1200	2400	3000	3500
1550 (1952-53), 104 SEL				
750	1100	2300	2900	3400
1500-A (1953-54), 104 SEL				
850	1500	2500	3200	3800
1550-A (1953-54), 104 SEL				
800	1400	2400	3000	3600
1600 (1953), 48 SEL				
450	900	1500	2250	2800
1650 (1953), 48 SEL				
400	850	1400	2150	2600
1600-A (1953-54), 48 SEL				
450	900	1500	2250	2800
1650-A (1954), 48 SEL				
400	850	1400	2150	2600
1600-AF (1953-54), 48 SEL HI-FI				
500	900	1500	2250	2800
1650-AF (1954), 48 SEL HI-FI				
450	850	1450	2200	2700
1700 (1954), 104 SEL				
2000	2750	3500	4000	4500
1700 HF (1954), 104 SEL HI-FI				
2000	2750	3500	4000	4500

GRADE 5	GRADE 4	GRADE 3	GRADE 2	GRADE 1
1800 (1955), 104 SEL				
2000	2750	3500	4200	5000
1900 (1955-56), 104 SEL				
2000	2750	3500	4200	5000
2000 (1956), 200 SEL (with pages)				
3500	4500	5500	6000	7000
2100 (1957), 200 SEL (with pages)				
3500	4400	5300	5800	6700
2104 (1957), 104 SEL				
2000	2750	3500	4200	5000
2150 (1957), 200 SEL				
800	1400	2000	2400	3000
2200, 2200-S (1958), 200 SEL, S=STEREO				
800	1400	2000	2500	3200
2204, 2204-S (1958), 104 SEL, S=STEREO				
800	1300	1900	2400	3000
2250 (1958), 200 SEL				
800	1400	2000	2500	3200
2300, 2300-S (1959), 200 SEL, S=STEREO				
850	1500	2000	2750	3500
2304, 2304-S (1959), 104 SEL, S=STEREO				
800	1400	1900	2600	3300
2310, 2310-S (1959), 100 SEL, S=STEREO				
800	1300	1800	2500	3200
2400, 2400-S (1960), 200 SEL, S=STEREO				
800	1500	1900	2700	3400
2404, 2404-S (1960), 104 SEL, S=STEREO				
750	1400	1800	2600	3300
2410, 2410-S (1960), 100 SEL, S=STEREO				
700	1300	1800	2500	3200

GRADE 5	GRADE 4	GRADE 3	GRADE 2	GRADE 1
2500, 2500-S (1961), 200 SEL, S=STEREO				
800	1500	2000	2500	3000
2504, 2504-S (1961), 104 SEL, S=STEREO				
800	1400	1900	2400	2900
2510, 2510-S (1961), 100 SEL, S=STEREO				
800	1300	1800	2300	2800
2600 (1962), 200 SEL				
700	900	1350	1750	2400
2610 (1962), 100 SEL				
600	800	1250	1600	2200
2700 (1963), 200 SEL				
700	900	1350	1750	2400
2710 (1963), 100 SEL				
700	800	1250	1600	2200
2800 (1964), 200 SEL				
700	850	1250	1600	2300
2810 (1964), 100 SEL				
650	800	1100	1450	2100
2900 (1965), 200 SEL				
700	850	1250	1600	2300
2910 (1965), 100 SEL				
650	800	1100	1450	2100
3000 (1966), 200 SEL				
700	850	1250	1600	2300
3010 (1966), 100 SEL				
650	800	1100	1450	2100
1050 WURL (1973), [1600], 100 SEL, NOSTALGIC MODEL				
2750	3500	4000	4500	5500

ADDENDUM TO GRADING SYSTEM

When we first published the first edition of this price guide in 1982 we did not include any jukebox models from the fifties. We designed our grading system and formula around the more collectible models of the forties. Now with the inclusion of the more metal and chrome models of the 50's and 60's we would like to make you aware of the following:

The five grades and **most** of the grading specifications still apply to these models. The formula giving 60% value to the cosmetics and 40% to the mechanics is still very much relevant. There are however a few things unique to 50's and 60's models that you would want to consider.

I. **Cosmetics** - Most of the fifties models have a lot more parts on the outside than on the inside that exhibit wear and abuse, so perhaps a little more attention will be needed here.

A. **Case** - The cabinets are important but not nearly as much as the older models of the forties. Many cabinets have a simulated wood finish, whether it be a decal, painted on or vinyl. Restoring these to original condition is not always needed or even desirable. The key is to offer the buyer or collector a professionally redone cabinet that is attractive and consistent with the original finish or design when you are restoring a box to either Grade 1 or Grade 2 condition.

B. **Plastics** - Most fifties models use some plastics with the earlier models using more that the later ones. As with all jukeboxes you will look for cracked, shrunken or otherwise damaged plastics when evaluating a machine.

Reproduction plastics and other parts are becoming more available for the Wurlitzer and Seeburg models of the fifties and these are fine to use (if of excellent quality) when restoring the box. Machines with cracked plastics are definitely going to be in the Grade 3 to 5 categories.

C. **Trim** - All models seem to have a lot of chrome plated trim castings. The rules outlined in our grading system to follow also apply here. The one notation might be to say that there will be less of the fifites models that will need to have the metal replated than of the earlier models. This is due in part to the newer state of the machines as well as to an increased use of chrome over nickel plating by the manufacturers of these machines.

Any parts that may have been woodgrained (i.e., Wurlitzer 1400 front door) should use rules already outlined.

II. **Mechanics** - Most aspects involving the mechanical components, electrical components and interior of the machine are the same as with earlier models. Follow the guidelines already laid out in the Grading System specifications with the following notations:

A. **Record Playing Mechanism** - Some models such as Seeburgs have mechanisms that do not lend themselves to easy cleaning. When restoring these, do the best you can. It is nice sometimes to totally dismantle a mechanism and totally clean and rebuild it - other times it is totally impractical and a step in the wrong direction to attempt to do so. This depends on the machine and to the extent that it needs it.

B. **Sound System** - Same criteria as thirties and forties models. Replace all worn needles and cartridges with best available when restoring the machine.

C. **Coin Mechanism** - Same as other except most fifties models used various coin denominations (i.e., 3 plays for quarter, 4 plays for quarter). This does not effect the value of the jukebox no matter what grade.

D. **Wiring** - When restoring most fifties models one finds that most of the electrical wiring is in very good condition. Replace as needed on restored machines.

E. **Cabinet Interior** - Interior wood panels often times clean up like new. If not so, repaint as needed for restored Grade 1 or 2 machines. All metal parts use guidelines already outlined in the main text.

GRADING SYSTEM

We have already commented on the problems inherent in pricing a machine in a particular state of condition. That is only one side of the coin, I'm afraid. The other is how do we agree on the various states of condition? We all know how abused the terms excellent, restored and mint have become. It seems that we can never agree on these terms without an argument arising.

It is in this sense (and for good sense) that we must adopt a set of guidelines for the grading of our machines. These basic guidelines outlined below along with the use of a formula will enable everyone to better communicate with one another about the condition of his/her machine.

First of all, we must consider the jukebox as being a combination of 2 separate but interlocking sections. The exterior section or **cosmetic** part and the interior section or functional **mechanical** part. By adopting a formula to equally assign a value to each of these sections we can get a more accurate value of each machine. The so-called cosmetic only restoration can now be put into perspective with relation to **fully** restored boxes. The formula that we will use is as follows:

$$G = \frac{3C + 2M}{5}$$

G meaning the final grade.
C meaning **cosmetics** and the cabinet.
M meaning the interior **mechanics** of the machine.

With this formula we are assigning 60% of the value to the outside restoration and 40% to the interior restoration of the machine. Thus if you have a machine with say a Grade 1 exterior (cosmetic) restoration but only a Grade 3 interior restoration you would come up with

$$G = \frac{(3 \times 1) + (2 \times 3)}{5} = 9/5 = 1.8$$

(A 1.8 grade could then be interpolated using the prices listed. If grade 1 is $5,000 and grade 2 is $4,000 - this machine would be worth approximately $4,200.

Grade 1 represents the perfect restoration while Grade 5 represents those boxes that are in the worst condition, yet still restorable.

Here now are our grading specifications for Grades 1 through 5. Remember that the following criteria will vary slightly with the box in question.

GRADE 1

This is the highest level of quality obtainable. It represents only those restored machines that look and operate as if they were still new.

I **Cosmetics** — Here we are concerned with the wood case and all exterior parts of the machine such as plastics, metal trim and glass. In order to qualify for a Grade 1 rating the following must apply.

  A. **Case** — The cabinet of the machine must be in perfect shape. The veneer must be original and not chipped, lifted, or marred in anyway. A few minor patches are allowed as long as the veneer is of a close match and does not show except at a very close distance. Up to 3 minor chips or dents are allowed in solid wood portions of the cabinet such as the base or the feet of a 1015 front door.

     The finish on the cabinet must be applied with the highest level of craftsmanship. The finish whether it be sprayed - lacquer or a hand-rubbed finish is up to the individual. The important factor is that it bring out the beauty of the wood and be very close to original quality.

     Stains must be applied only where originally used, such as along trim areas around plastics. The back and bottom of the machine (along with all inside cabinet surfaces) must be repainted or stained as original.

  B. **Plastics** — Plastics are used on most of the more desirable machines. These must be originals with no cracks, chips, or burn marks or reproductions if they are of original quality. (With Wurlitzer 1015's, the reproductions are usually better than the originals). They must be cleaned and/or polished to the highest standards. If the plastics were originally white such as Wurlitzer Models 700, 750, 800, 850 they must be sanded down to the original color, repolished and repainted as originals. Shrunken plastics with more than a 1/8″ gap are not allowed in this grade. Neither are colored plastics (such as green) which have faded in color.

  C. **Trim** — Here we are dealing with the rest of the exterior of the jukebox. This consists of any nickel-plated trim pieces and all other metal and glass parts on the front and sides of the machine.

     All parts originally nickel-plated must be replated unless in absolutely new condition with no noticeable wear or pitting. Replated parts may be either nickel or chrome plated as long as they are relatively free of pitting and polished so they are smooth to the touch. Good platers are hard to find, so shop around. Broken or welded parts are not allowed in Grade 1. Aluminum castings can either be plated or polished (polishing preferred). Any brass parts must be polished and lacquered to prevent tarnishing.

Any metal parts that were originally wood grained must be refinished by a professional wood-grainer. Painting is not allowed where a grain was originally present.

All other parts such as silk-screened plastics and glass pieces must be of near new quality with no noticeable wear. Reproductions are allowed only if the quality is equal to the originals.

II Mechanics

This includes the complete inner workings of the machine. The record playing mechanism, coin mechanism, sound system, animation assemblies and all wiring are the key elements found here:

A. **Record Playing Mechanism** — The main mechanism of the machine must be completely cleaned and rebuilt. On Wurlitzer machines the stack must be totally disassembled, all trays cleaned and polished and reassembled with proper lubricants. The wood deck or shelf must be refinished or repainted as required. The remainder of the mechanism must be steam-cleaned and degreased. Any parts originally nickel-plated must be replated unless perfect original with a high lustre. This includes all bolts, washers, posts, tonearms, etc. On Wurlitzer machines the tonearm may or may not be chrome plated depending on personal preference. If not plated, then it must be polished. The turntable must be reflocked.

All worn parts including cams, bushings, and gears must be replaced or rebuilt to original specs. The mechanism when installed in the restored machine must work flawlessly, quietly and resemble mint condition.

B. **Sound System** — The tonearm must be repacked if of the original magnetic type. Arms with a crystal or ceramic cartridge should have the cartridge replaced. Any worn cable leads must be replaced. The amplifier must be totally rebuilt with new capacitors, resistors, etc. where needed. Tubes can be original. The amplifier should be repainted unless in excellent shape. The speaker must be totally cleaned and be free of any tears in the cone. Reconed speakers are allowed. The sound should be the heart of a good restoration. If your machine does not have the bass and volume it should it's not Grade 1.

C. **Coin Mechanism** — The complete coin mechanism must be intact. It must be thoroughly overhauled and cleaned and work flawlessly. It must not be altered from original specs. (i.e., 1 play for 5¢, 5 for 25¢).

D. **Wiring** — All cloth covered wire or other frayed wires must be replaced with original type wire. This is done not only for aesthetic reasons, but for safety reasons.

E. **Cabinet Interior** — The inside of the cabinet must be restored to like new condition. This includes repainting all painted areas including coin boards, speaker doors, and curtains. Use original color paint only. All other control units, steppers, animation assemblies, etc. must be in excellent condition or repainted with new markings present. Any metal parts that show signs of rust must be sandblasted and cadmium plated or painted silver. Rusted screws should be replaced with new ones. The selection system must work flawlessly in this grade. The inside of the Grade 1 jukebox should appear as new as the outside. It must be free of all dirt, rust, and other matter. It must be 100% complete and all functional parts operational. Reproduction parts are allowed if they look and match original quality.

GRADE 2

This grade represents machines that I would consider the average "very good" restoration. The jukebox looks beautiful, works well and to all but the perfectionist is fully restored.

I **Cosmetics**

Most of the criteria for Grade 1 apply here also, but there are a number of **exceptions** that will make the machine less desirable than a Grade 1 restoration.

A. **Case** — Here again the cabinet must be totally refinished as in Grade 1, but part of the cabinet can be reveneered **if done properly**. All veneer must be of the same type originally used and must be flat when glued down - ripples or seams don't make it. Again a few patches are allowed if patched properly. Finish is up to the individual as long as it feels smooth to the touch. Up to 5 small dents are allowed in solid wood pieces. If the finish is mint original (no cracking) it is allowed in this grade (very few qualify). The inside of the cabinet should be painted as well as the back of the machine. Coin boards, bottom of the cabinet, etc. do not have to be painted, if they are still in excellent condition.

Stains must be used according to original specifications only (i.e. no walnut stain on a 1080).

B. **Plastics** — Plastics on Grade 2 cabinets must be free from cracks or outside chips. Shrinkage is again limited to no more than 1/8" at either end. Wurlitzer models 700, 750, 800 & 850 may still have the plastics left in a "yellow" finish as long as they are cleaned and the inside painting is intact. Reproductions are allowed again only if they match original quality and design. Some fading is allowed on green plastics (700, 800, 850 sides), but not on red plastics. No burn marks over 1/2" in diameter may be present.

C. **Trim** — Nickel or chrome plated again should be replated unless they are free of pitting and exhibit a high lustre when polished. Interior plated parts may or may not be replated depending on condition. Up to 2 breaks that have been properly welded will be allowed in Grade 2.

Aluminum and any other exterior parts not painted or plated should be polished. Wood grained metal parts must be redone to resemble the original effect. They do not have to be professionally wood-grained, but cannot be painted a flat brown.

All other plastic and glass silk-screened parts must be in excellent shape. Reproductions are allowed whenever of excellent quality.

II Mechanics

A. **Record Playing Mechanism** — The specifications here are the same as for a Grade 1 mechanism except:

1) The stack does not have to be totally disassembled so long as the trays swing out freely with no binding. The rest of the mechanism must be thoroughly cleaned and appear in excellent condition with new post and tray decals where needed.

2) Cams, rollers, and bushings may be slightly worn so long as the mechanism still operates properly. The main drive gear must fit tight with no other noticeable wear or slippage.

3) The mechanism shelf (whether wood or metal) may or may not be refinished if in near original condition with a high lustre finish.

B. **Sound System** — The restoration of the sound system components (tonearm, volume control, amp and speaker) are just as important in a Grade 2 restoration as Grade 1. The same criteria apply here as in Grade 1.

C. **Coin Mechanism** — All coin mechanisms must be intact and fully operational. Reproduction parts are allowed here so long as they function and resemble original equipment. Coin slides where used, may or may not be replated (Grade 1 slides must be renickeled).

D. **Wiring** — Electrical wiring does not have to be totally replaced in this grade except where it is noticeably worn, frayed or cracked. All cracked plugs or sockets should be replaced.

E. **Cabinet Interior** — The interior of the machine must be thoroughly cleaned and be free of any accumulaton of dirt and grease. It may be repainted, but does not have to be if it is not very worn.
All metal mounting brackets must be cleaned or sandblasted with no visible rust. Junction boxes, animation assemblies, steppers, etc. may have some small scratches present and exhibit normal wear. Parts that show deterioration must be repainted accordingly. The overall appearance must be clean, dust-free, and very close to the criteria outlined in Grade 1.

GRADE 3

This grade represents machines of 2 types. The first of these is what I would call machines that are of an excellent original condition. They are full of dirt inside, but over-all exhibit an appearance of being well preserved (good cabinets, chrome, plastics, complete and working well). They are above average in their unrestored state, but could be made much closer to perfect if they were restored and cleaned.

The second type of box that falls into this pricing category is what I would call the average "amateur" restoration. A box may still be called "restored" by the restorer, but there are obvious differences between this machine and a Grade 1 or a Grade 2 restored machine. The term reconditioned comes into my mind more than totally restored when I see a box such as this. A brief summation of a Grade 3 restored machine is as follows:

I **Cosmetics**
Here we will notice some differences from Grades 1 and 2 as

previously described, though the major discrepancies will be in the area of mechanics and the interior of the machine.

A. **Case** — The cabinet of the machine will usually have some veneer work done to it and one will find upon close examination a lack of skill in how the veneer has been replaced or repaired. It may have ripples in it and there may be areas of the cabinet where patches were needed but not even used such as the back edges on the cabinet.

The finish may be rough to the touch or look like a sheet of glass, if a high gloss polyurethane is used. Overall the finish may be fine, but it usually is put on prior to correcting problems in the wood.

It is also not uncommon to see the "average" restoration with a coat of walnut or other stain applied to the cabinet where it wasn't needed.

As for painting the inside of the machine, it usually isn't done in Grade 3. The back of the box may be painted. "After all who looks at the back and the insides anyway says the restorer?"

B. **Plastics** — Here we find the plastics usually in their original state. Most are not properly cleaned or repainted in the Wurlitzer line of 500 through 850 models. One of the main plastics may have a crack in it. With Wurlitzer Models 1015 and 1080, we usually still see the whole set being replaced. This is done mostly out of necessity (as opposed to choice) because the overall condition of the original plastics was bad. Some 1015's and 1080's may still have the original plastics intact, but a few cracks or shrinkage will be present.

C. **Trim** — Metal castings on a Grade 3 machine are not usually replated. They have been polished and the nickel finish still exhibits a good lustre. Overall the trim on this box looks very good, but a purist would probably have it replated.

II **Mechanics** — As mentioned above, the interior and mechanical aspects of this grade machine will vary more than the cosmetics when compared to Grade 2.

A. **Record Playing Mechanism** — Obvious comments about a mechanism in this condition would be - it works OK, it looks clean on top, it's greasy on the bottom - what more needs to be done? The important criteria for grade 1 and even grade 2 are overlooked here. The mechanism is not disassembled, steam cleaned, and it probably works with a few problems.

The mechanism shelf if made of wood is probably not refinished. The nickel plated parts are probably not replated. The turntable may or may not be reflocked. The mechanism seems to function properly but little has been done to restore it to like new condition.

B. **Sound System** — Overall sound reproduction is still quite good, but little more has been done than to wipe off the amp and tonearm and rebuild the amplifier if it needed it. Usually lacking are such things as repacking the tonearm (if original), repainting the amplifier and thoroughly rebuilding the amplifier. The machine may be equipped with a lightweight pick-up and produce a rather "tinny" sound as no modification was done to compensate for the change in pick-up.

C. **Coin Mechanism** — Sometimes present, sometimes gone -that best describes this grade machine. With machines such as a 1015 the grinder and slug rejector are usually gone. If they are intact they usually are dirty and not always accepting coins the way they were meant to. With models that use coin slides on the outside of the box, these must be intact even if the coin mechansim inside the box is absent.

D. **Wiring** — Electrical wiring is not normally redone on this grade of machine, but we wouldn't expect to find any bare wires either.

E. **Cabinet Interior** — The balance of the cabinet interior like the mechanism will be lacking in detailed cleaning. The painted items such as junction boxes, animation assemblies, metal brackets will be only partially cleaned. Some rust and scratches will be present and signs of dirt and grease will be evident where some interior parts will be left intact instead of being removed and cleaned. Overall the machine will be relatively complete and functional but it may look more like it was cleaned in a few hours instead of a few days. Minor parts such as covers, clamps, screws, etc. may be missing and some parts may exhibit wear like rubber bushings, grill cloth, plastic trim, etc. A nice box for its age but not "mint restored."

GRADE 4

This grade represents machines that I would commonly refer to as average or good unrestored. Little or no reconditioning has been done here. The machine may or may not work. It must be basicly complete so as to function properly with no major components missing. Coin mechanism being usually present, but not a neccessity. A Grade 4 machine is your average good unrestored box that can be restored to mint condition with your normal restoration procedures. Some unknowledgable persons may call this box "excellent" for its age, but you the experienced restorer, know better. General characteristics of this grade jukebox follow:

I **Cosmetics** — Overall appearance will be dirty, worn, some scratches, minor veneer damage to cabinet.

    A. **Case** — The veneer must be at least 75% intact and the basic wood cabinet solid. It may have been slightly damp at one time in its life but not in a flood. Loose veneer will usually be found on the lower sides, on the back, or on any curved portions of the cabinet. It may be able to be reglued, but more than likely it will have to be replaced when properly restored. The finish will be worn and without question stripped and refinished. Metal parts that have a wood grain finish will also usually exhibit increased wear and will have to be refinished to match the wood.

    Overall a good cabinet to restore but it will take some time to do it right.

    B. **Plastics** — Plastics on Wurlitzer models 1015 and 1080 being a thinner type of material will need to be replaced. Obvious cracks, shrinkage and peeling of the paint will make this necessary. Since the reproductions on the market today are of excellent quality, this will pose no problem to maintaining original specifications.

    On models with heavy plastics such as Rock-Ola's, Mills and pre-war Wurlitzers you can expect on the average to have at least one of the main plastics to be cracked or of an earlier replacement (Wico, Acme, etc.)

    C. **Trim** — Look forward to having all the metal trim renickeled if you want the box restored to Grade 1. The average unrestored machine will exhibit worn plating and some pitts in the finish. You can try and polish it, but results will usually yield less than desired results. On pre-war Wurlitzers like the 850 you can expect at least one trim piece to be cracked. One is acceptable. The balance of the cabinet trim should be in good condition with no rust and pretty much complete. All screened glass pieces should be in good condition without cracks.

II **Mechanics** — Here we are more concerned with missing parts than with whether it works or not.

A. **Record Playing Mechanism** — It should be complete with motor, selector unit, etc. It may work but will probably not operate like it should without some adjustments, cleaning and oiling. The main fiber gear in a Wurlitzer machine may even be stripped out. Don't worry as long as there are no major parts gone nor major problems evident such as cracks in the frame, etc. As for wear if it stayed in the United States its probably got a long life ahead of it. If it came from Mexico, skip this section and go directly to Grade 5.

B. **Sound System** — Again in this condition we are more concerned with completeness. The volume control unit, amplifier, tonearm, and speaker must all be present. The cartridge can be bad and the speaker can even have a hole in the cone, but they must be in the machine. Don't expect it to sound like you remembered.

C. **Coin Mechanism** — Usually intact, but not always. If absent totally you must tend to value the machine a little less (about 10%) you will need it if you want to restore the machine so think about where you can find one (if at all) before you buy the machine. Coin slides and coin grinders for Wurlitzers bring a premium.

D. **Wiring** — All selection wiring and electrical wiring should be intact and working. Plan on rewiring the electrical portion of the machine.

E. **Cabinet Interior** — Overall it will be dirty, greasy, some dust and wear on metal and painted surfaces. As with Grade 3 you will find minor items usually gone such as clamps, covers, screws, etc. Basic components such as the junction box, relay box, animation units, etc. will still be intact. A few minor items may be missing such as a cashbox, oil pan, color cylinder, motor or cage. These items are reproduced and pose no real problem to completing the box.
You can expect a thorough over-haul of the inside will be needed with new paint and a lot of elbow work. After all this box probably hasn't been touched inside for 30 years or so.

A good rule of thumb is that the average good unrestored machine (Grade 4), is worth about one-half of the price of a mint restored box (Grade 1). This of course is only a general guideline and will vary with the cost of the restoration involved. Some boxes cost more to restore than others.

GRADE 5

This classification represents the worst of the machines that can still be considered restorable. They might have been considered "junkers" about 5 years ago, today these are fair unrestored machines that may require a good deal of cabinet work and an above average amount of replacement parts, but they still can be restored to a Grade 2 condition if the work is put into the machine.

I **Cosmetics**

In a Grade 5 you can't expect the jukebox to look like much. It's had a rough life and it shows it. Obvious characteristics are as follows:

A. **Case** — The veneer is usually lifted in several places on the front and sides of the box. In fact the whole box may have to be reveneered, but usually around 50% of the cabinet will need reglueing. The finish is obviously gone.

The cabinet has usually seen a good deal of wear and tear and a good amount of moisture. It didn't sit out in the rain but it may have sat in a barn for a few years.

Count on spending an above average amount of time on reveneering and glueing the main wood joints. If the box has come from Mexico look for possible termite damage.

B. **Plastics** — Again don't count on too much especially with the thinner type 1015 and 1080 plastics. They will without a doubt need replacing. Machines with the heavy type plastics as in 750 and 850 Wurlitzers, you can expect to have several of these broken. New reproduction plastics are normally required for Grade 5 machines if available.

C. **Trim** — The nickel plated trim pieces will be worn and pitted. A couple of the pieces may be cracked and will have to be welded. With an experienced plater you can still make the trim look like new so don't worry too much. It should be basicly complete. Glass windows will need replacing as they tend to get broken out. The rest of the cabinet trim pieces should be worn but complete.

II **Mechanics** — "As is — Usually not working, minor parts gone", that best sums up the mechanics of a Grade 5 machine.

A. **Record Playing Mechanism** — Look for a basically complete mechanism. Parts usually remain intact on the main mechanism. If anything is gone, it will probably be the motor. Look for a greasy, dirty jammed up piece of machinery. If it does cycle it will undoubtedly need a good deal of adjusting. You can expect the mechanism mounting board (if wood) to have some loose veneer. Nickel plated parts will be worn and tarnished and several pieces may exhibit rust.

B. **Sound System** — Look for it. If your amplifier, tonearm, volume control and speaker are all intact you're in luck. Sound systems tend to be the first thing robbed along with coin units when operators look for parts to take out of their machines. You can expect to overhaul everything in a Grade 5 sound system. Repaint that rusty looking amplifier, recone that torn speaker, replace the tonearm cartridge and repaint the volume control. Don't expect it to play when you find it as is.

C. **Coin Mechanism** — Any or all of it may be intact. However with Wurlitzers you can expect the coin slides and coin grinders to be gone. Operators didn't believe in selling a used machine for home use with a coin mechanism intact. Unfortunately some of todays restorers still follow the same policy.

D. **Wiring** — You will need to replace all main electrical wiring unless you sell fire insurance. Plastic coated and rayon coated wires get frayed and they will be needing replacements. As for selector harness wiring it will probably also need a little attention to work properly.

E. **Cabinet Interior** — Look for other items to be gone including heaters, animation assemblies, oil pans, back doors, covers, etc. The more complete - the more this machine will bring. Many of these items, especially for Wurlitzers are reproduced, but you will have to figure the added cost into the restoration, so count before you buy.
The overall appearance of the interior will be dirty, greasy, paint worn and some loose veneer inside as well as outside. Decorative panels and other silk screened parts will exhibit more wear and may need to be replaced. You can count on spending a little more time restoring the inside of this machine, as well as money.

AMI
PHONOGRAPHS

◀ AMI
MODEL A

Height	60	"
Width	36	"
Depth	24	"
Weight	300 lbs.	
Records	20	

AMI
Model B ▶

Height	70	"
Width	32	"
Depth	24	"
Weight	260 lbs.	
Records	20	

◀ AMI
Model C

Height	66½"	
Width	33¼"	
Depth	24⅝"	
Weight	253 lbs.	
Records	20	

AMI ▶
Model D-40
1951-52
40 SEL 78 RPM
(80 SEL 45 RPM)

AMI
MODEL D-80
1951-52
80 SEL 45 RPM

AMI
Model E
1953
40 SEL 78 RPM
80 SEL 45 RPM
120 SEL 45 RPM

AMI
Model F
1954
40 SEL 78 RPM
80 SEL 45 RPM
120 SEL 45 RPM

AMI
Model G
1955
80 SEL 45 RPM
120 SEL 45 RPM

AMI
Model G-200
1956
200 SEL 45 RPM

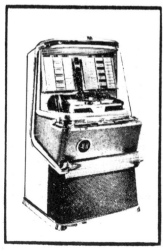

AMI
Model H-100
1957
100 SEL 45 RPM

AMI
Model H-120
1957
120 SEL 45 RPM

AMI
Model H-200
1957
200 SEL 45 RPM

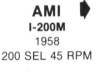

AMI
Model I-200
1958
200 SEL 45 RPM

AMI
I-200M
1958
200 SEL 45 RPM

AMI
Model 1-120
1958
120 SEL 45 RPM
Model I-100
1958
100 SEL 45 RPM

AMI
Model J
1959
(Mono/Stereo)
200, 120, 100 SEL
45 RPM

 AMI
Model K
1960
200, 120, 100 SEL
45 RPM

AMI ▶
Lyric 1960
100 SEL 45 RPM

◀ **AMI**
Continental
1960 - 200 SEL
45 RPM

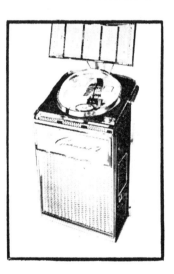

AMI ▶
Continental 2
1961
200 or 100 SEL
45 RPM

◀ **AMI**
Models JAL/JEL
1963
200, 120, 100 SEL
45 RPM

AMI ▶
Tropicana
1963-64
200,160, 100 SEL
45 RPM

ROCK-OLA
PHONOGRAPHS

◀ ROCKOLA
12-Record

Height	50	"
Width	28	"
Depth	21	"
Records	12	

ROCKOLA ▶
16-Record

Height	51	"
Width	28	"
Depth	21	"
Records	16	

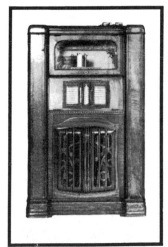

◀ ROCKOLA
Rhythm King - 16

Height	51 ¾	"
Width	32 ¼	"
Depth	23 ¾	"
Records	16	

ROCKOLA
Imperial 20

Height	52	"
Width	32 ¾	"
Depth	23	"
Records	20	▶

ROCKOLA
Windsor

Height	53 ½"
Width	28 "
Depth	23 ½"
Records	20

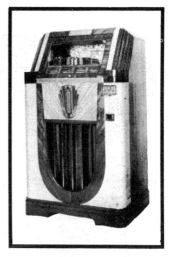

ROCKOLA
Monarch

Height	55 ⅝"
Width	32 ⅞"
Depth	23 ½"
Records	20

ROCKOLA
'39 Counter

Height	22 ¾"
Width	24 "
Depth	20 ¾"
Records	12

ROCKOLA
'39 Standard

Height	55 ½"
Width	34 ¼"
Depth	25 ½"
Records	20

ROCKOLA
'39 DeLuxe

Height	56 "
Width	38 "
Depth	25 ½"
Records	20

ROCKOLA
'40 Super (W)

Height	67 ½"
Width	38 "
Depth	25 ½"
Records	20

ROCKOLA
'40 Master (W)

Height	54½"
Width	35½"
Depth	24 "
Records	20

ROCKOLA
'40 Master Rockolite

Height	55¼"
Width	34 "
Depth	24½"
Records	20

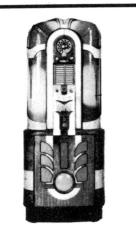

ROCKOLA
'41 Premier

Height	66½"
Width	28 "
Depth	26 "
Records	20

ROCKOLA
'42 Commando

Height	72¼"
Width	33 "
Depth	25½"
Records	20

Playmaster, hideaway record changer operates with one or more Spectrovox speaker - selectors

ROCKOLA
Playmaster

Height	37¼"
Width	28 "
Depth	21½"
Records	20

ROCKOLA
Spectrovox

Height	73 "
Width	28 "
Depth	28 "

◀ ROCKOLA
Model 1422

Height   58   "
Width   29¾"
Depth   26   "
Weight   342 lbs.
Records 20

ROCKOLA ▶
Model 1426

Height   57¾"
Width   30   "
Depth   26   "
Weight   338 lbs.
Records 20

◀ ROCKOLA
Model 1428

Height   60½"
Width   30   "
Depth   26   "
Weight   354 lbs.
Records 20

ROCKOLA ▶
Model 1432
Rocket 1950
50 SEL

◀ ROCKOLA
Model 1434
Super Rocket
1950-52
50 SEL

ROCKOLA ▶
Model 1436
Fireball 1952
120 SEL 45 RPM

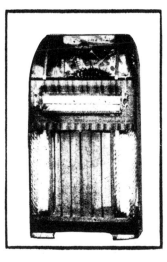

ROCKOLA
Model 1438
Comet 1954
120 SEL 45 RPM

ROCKOLA
Model 1442
1954
50 SEL 45 RPM

ROCKOLA
Model 1446
1954
120 SEL 45 RPM

ROCKOLA
Model 1448
1955
120 SEL 45 RPM

ROCKOLA
Model 1452
1956
50 SEL 45 RPM

ROCKOLA
Model 1454
1956
120 SEL 45 RPM

◀ **ROCKOLA**
Model 1455
1957
200 SEL 45 RPM

ROCKOLA ▶
Model 1458
1958
120 SEL 45 RPM

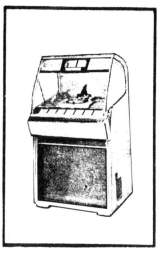

◀ **ROCKOLA**
Model 1462
1958
50 SEL 45 RPM

ROCKOLA ▶
Model 1464
1958
Wall Type Phono

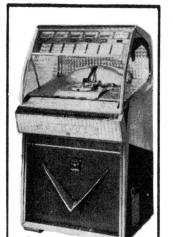

◀ **ROCKOLA**
Model 1465
1958
200 SEL 45 RPM

ROCKOLA ▶
Model 1475
1959
200 SEL
Model 1468
120 SEL

ROCKOLA
Model 1485
1960
200 SEL
Model 1478
120 SEL

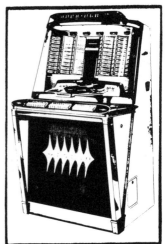

ROCKOLA
Model 1495
1961
200 SEL
Model 1488
120 SEL

ROCKOLA
Model 1493
Princess
1961
100 SEL

ROCKOLA
Model 1484
1961 Wall Model
100 SEL

ROCKOLA
MODEL 1497
Empress 1962
200 SEL
Model 1496
120 SEL

ROCKOLA
Model 408
Rhapsody 1963
160 SEL
Model 404 Capri
100 SEL

ROCKOLA
Model 418 SA
Rhapsody II 1964
160 SEL
Model 414
Capri II
100 SEL

ROCKOLA
Model 424
Princess Royal
1964
100 SEL

ROCKOLA
Model 425
Grand Prix 1964
100 SEL

ROCKOLA
Model 426
Grand Prix II
1965
160 SEL

ROCKOLA
MODEL 429
Starlet 1965
100 SEL

ROCKOLA
Model 432
GP-160
1966-67
160 SEL

SEEBURG
PHONOGRAPHS

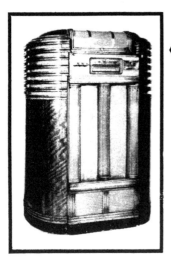

SEEBURG
Concert Grand

Height	60	"
Width	42	"
Depth	23	"
Records	20	

SEEBURG
Symphonola

Height	49	"
Width	30	"
Depth	21 ½	"
Records	12	

SEEBURG
Rex

Height	50 ¼	"
Width	31	"
Depth	23 ¼	"
Records	20	

SEEBURG
K-20

Height	54 ½	"
Width	35 ½	"
Depth	25 ⅝	"
Records	20	

SEEBURG
Royale

Height	54 ¾ "
Width	35 "
Depth	23 ½ "
Records	20

SEEBURG
Plaza

Height	53 "
Width	36 ¼ "
Depth	23 ¼ "
Records	20

SEEBURG
Regal

Height	55 ¼ "
Width	38 "
Depth	22 ¼ "
Records	20

SEEBURG
Gem

Height	50 ¾ "
Width	30 ¼ "
Depth	22 ¼ "
Records	20

SEEBURG
Classic

Height	55 ½ "
Width	36 ¼ "
Depth	24 ¾ "
Records	20

SEEBURG
Mayfair

Height	55 "
Width	40 ¼ "
Depth	23 ¼ "
Records	20

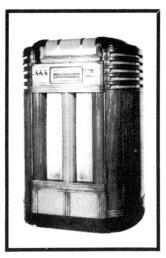

SEEBURG
Crown

Height	56	"
Width	38	"
Depth	21 ¾	"
Records	20	

SEEBURG
Cadet

Height	55 ¼	"
Width	34	"
Depth	25	"
Records	20	

SEEBURG
Major

Height	55 ½	"
Width	33	"
Depth	25 ¼	"
Records	20	

SEEBURG
Envoy

Height	53 ¾	"
Width	33 ½	"
Depth	26 ¾	"
Records	20	

SEEBURG
Vogue

Height	51 ¾	"
Width	32 ¾	"
Depth	25 ¼	"
Records	20	

SEEBURG
Casino

Height	51 ¼	"
Width	32 ¼	"
Depth	23 ¼	"
Records	20	

SEEBURG
Commander

Height	59 ½ "
Width	36 ½ "
Depth	24 ½ "
Records	20

SEEBURG
Model 9800

Height	66 ½ "
Width	36 ½ "
Depth	27 "
Records	20

SEEBURG
Model 8800

Height	63 ¼ "
Width	34 ¼ "
Depth	28 "
Records	20

SEEBURG
Model 8200

Height	62 ½ "
Width	33 ¼ "
Depth	28 "
Records	20

SEEBURG
**20 Record
'43 Cab.**

Height	62 "
Width	33 ¼ "
Depth	28 "
Records	20

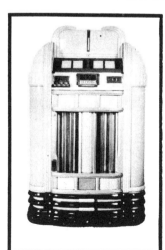

SEEBURG
Colonel

Height	59 ½ "
Width	36 ¼ "
Depth	24 ½ "
Records	20

SEEBURG
Model 146

Height	57	"
Width	36	"
Depth	26½"	
Weight	355 lbs.	
Records	20	

SEEBURG ▶
Model 147

Height	57	"
Width	37	"
Depth	26½"	
Weight	317 lbs.	
Records	20	

◀ SEEBURG
Model 148

Height	57	"
Width	37	"
Depth	26½"	
Weight	325 lbs.	
Records	20	

SEEBURG ▶
Model 100-J/JL
1955
100 SEL 45 RPM

◀
SEEBURG
Model M100A
1949
100 SEL 78 RPM

▶
SEEBURG
Model M100B/BL
1950-51
100 SEL 45 RPM

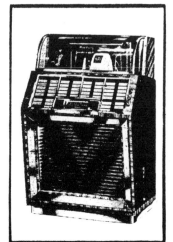